D1089097

In Harmony
and
Other Songs of Peace

by Sue Sheriff

illustrated by Arabella Eldredge

Pine & Chadwick
PUBLISHING

Pine and Chadwick Publishing
211 Marginal Way, Suite 136
Portland, Maine 04101-2438

Photography by Debbie Harmon; www.debbieharmonphotography.com

Text for "Peace Symbols and Peacemakers" written by Rebecca Hotaling

Prepared for publication by Jorlan Publishing
Cover design by Pamela Farrance
Interior design and typesetting by Marny K. Parkin
www.JorlanPublishing.com

CD production:
Produced and arranged by: Tom Acousti
www.TomAcousti.com
Engineers: Abel Adame, Tom Acousti
Asst. Engineer: Jess Pyle-Carter

Recorded and mixed at:
Sound Harbor Studios, Portland, Maine
www.SoundHarborMusic.com
Mastered by Eric Conn, Independent Mastering, Nashville, TN

Lead Vocals: Sue Sheriff; www.suesheriff.com
Harmony Vocals: Tom Acousti and Pauline Keenan
Kids Chorus: Kaicee Flaherty, Emily Keenan, Maggie Lamarre

Bass: Justin Maxwell
Drums: Sean Boissoneault
Guitars: Robbie Coffin
Keyboards: Bob Charest

Special thanks to Anne Belden and Kim Walsh for all their support.

Peace Pilgrim quote from *Peace Pilgrim—Her Life and Works in Her Own Words* (Friends of Peace Pilgrim and Ocean Tree Books, 1982), 132.

ISBN 978-0-9801845-0-1

Library of Congress Control Number: 2008921507

Printed in China

10 9 8 7 6 5 4 3 2 1

Part of the proceeds from the sale of this book will be donated to UNICEF

"Peace—a naïve concept in this world full of turmoil, disintegration, and societal fragmentation. Yet it is so vitally important that we strive for more acceptance of and a greater respect for others, and that this striving should lead to positive action. We need to respect and care for our earth which nurtures us with its natural beauty and glory. It is with heartfelt passion that I challenge you to consider thoughts, feelings, and actions that will contribute to global peace. Let us embrace peace in our daily lives and lead by example. In hope for peace, I dedicate this book to my husband, John, and our two sons, Iain and Macgill."

Arabella

"Peace is in every one of us. It is important to teach our children, from a very young age, to access their own inner peace so that they can have peaceful experiences in the world. We must also help them understand that we are all interconnected. That makes every person our brother or sister. And so we must learn to treat each other with love and respect. To me, these concepts are essential to creating world peace.

"My vision for *In Harmony and Other Songs of Peace* is to provide beautiful songs, with easily learned lyrics, as well as enchanting imagery, allowing children to more readily internalize the message of peace and more easily recall it in times of need. In addition to learning the music together, parents, teachers and children can use the activity pages in the back of this book to initiate discussions on peace and to explore a child's inner ability to be a peacemaker in his/her own world.

"A special thanks to my husband, Barry, who lifts me up and always supports my dreams. And I am so grateful for God's inner guidance and inspiration."

Sue

In harmony, that's how I'd like the world to be,
Living in peace and loving one another.

In harmony, we can all be free
By treating everyone like he's a brother.

And although we may have differences
That make us all unique . . .

We all want the same in life—
It's happiness we seek.

We all have different faces;
Thoughts and feelings, too.

*B*ut we all want a healthy earth
With skies and oceans blue.

*I*n harmony,
that's how I'd like the world to be,
Living in peace and loving one another.

In harmony,
we can all be free
By treating everyone like he's a brother.

*S*ome of us need a wheelchair
And some of us cannot hear.

*B*ut all we want is to be loved
And live life without fear.

Let's celebrate our differences,
Yet find our common ground.

We all deserve life's goodness—
There's enough to go around!

*I*n harmony,
that's how I'd like the world to be,
Living in peace and loving one another.

In harmony,
we can all be free
By treating everyone like he's a brother.

Symbols of Peace
Images from around the world express the hope for peace.

*T*he dove is one of the oldest peace symbols, dating back to the story of Noah and the Ark in the Bible. In this ancient tale of the Great Flood, it rained for 40 days and 40 nights, covering the entire world with water. Noah released a white dove in hopes that it would find dry land. The dove came back carrying an olive branch. It was a sign that the hard times were over and that a peaceful time had come. Since then, the dove and olive branch have symbolized a hope for peace.

*T*he most traditionally recognized peace symbol is a circle with a line running down the center and an upside down "V" near the bottom. It was originally designed by a British man named Gerald Holtom. The actual symbol is a combination of visual flag signals for the letters "N" and "D." These letters stand for *Nuclear Disarmament*. In the 1960s, the symbol came to represent the anti-war movement. Today, it simply represents peace.

*T*he peace sign is made by holding up the middle and index fingers to form the letter "V." Initially, this sign began in Europe during World War II when a "V" for victory was painted on walls as a symbol of freedom from occupying forces. During the protests against the Vietnam War, this gesture started to stand for peace. Anti-war protestors would make the V-sign and call out "peace," and since then, people all over the world use it.

sym•bol—something that stands for something else; especially something real that stands for or suggests another thing that cannot by itself be pictured or shown

*I*n 1955, a young Japanese girl named Sadako Sasaki became very sick from the bombing of Hiroshima. One of her best friends told her the legend that if a sick person folded one thousand paper cranes, he or she would get well again. Unfortunately, Sadako never did get well. However, her friends decided to build a monument for her and all the other children who were killed by the atom bomb. In 1958, a statue of Sadako holding a golden crane was erected in the Hiroshima Peace Park. Now paper cranes are a symbol for peace.

*T*he peace flag is a rainbow flag that represents peace. Rainbow flags have been displayed in many cultures around the world to express diversity, unity, and hope. First seen in 1961, this flag has all seven colors of the rainbow with the word "PACE" (pronounced PAH-chay) in white letters in the middle of it. "PACE" means "peace" in Italian. This flag was hung from millions of homes and workplaces all over Italy prior to the war against Iraq. It has become increasingly popular in Europe and the United States.

*T*he peace pipe, or medicine pipe, is a ceremonial smoking pipe used by many Native American tribes. They would put tobacco, which was considered sacred, into red-stoned pipes and smoke the pipes as a token of peace. As the Native Americans filled their pipes, prayers would be offered to the north, south, east, and west, to Mother Earth, and to Father Sky. It was considered respectful to blow smoke into the faces of those who were smoking the peace pipe with them. This gesture was a sign of the highest respect.

Thoughts on Peace

Mother Teresa (1910–1997)

"What can you do to promote world peace? Go home and love your family."

*M*other Teresa was a Roman Catholic nun who devoted over 40 years of her life to helping the poor, sick, orphaned, and dying in India. In 1979, she was awarded the Nobel Peace Prize for her humanitarian work. Today, over 4,000 nuns still carry on her work. She was named *Blessed Teresa of Calcutta* by Pope John Paul III, a most high honor.

Mohandas Gandhi (1869–1948)

"You must be the change you wish to see in the world."

*M*ohandas Gandhi was a spiritual and political leader in India. He promoted civil rights for his people by using the principle of *ahimsa,* or complete non-violence. His principles inspired civil rights movements all over the world. In India, he is recognized as *Father of the Nation* and is also called "Mahatma," which means "Great Soul."

Chief Seattle (1786–1866)

"We are part of the earth and the earth is part of us. All things are connected."

*C*hief Seattle was a leader of the Suquamish Native American tribe. Instead of fighting when white settlers threatened his tribe's lands, Chief Seattle befriended an influential pioneer who helped him advocate for Native American rights. In one of his most famous speeches, he called for peace, Native American rights, and respect for the environment.

from Famous Peacemakers

John Lennon (1940–1980)

"Imagine all the people living life in peace."

John Lennon was an English singer, songwriter, and musician who initially gained fame in the rock group, The Beatles. Lennon's song, *Give Peace a Chance,* was sung by half a million people at an anti-war protest in Washington, D.C., in 1969. Even today, many years after his death, Lennon is considered a peace activist.

Eleanor Roosevelt (1884–1962)

"It isn't enough to talk about peace; one must believe in it. And it isn't enough to believe in it; one must work at it."

Eleanor Roosevelt, the wife of President Franklin D. Roosevelt, was a world-renowned humanitarian dedicated to human rights, equality, tolerance and world peace. She was the first US delegate to the United Nations and Chairman of the Human Rights Commission. Voted the most admired woman in America for 13 consecutive years, Eleanor Roosevelt was recognized as *"The First Lady of the World."*

The Peace Pilgrim (1908–1981)

"When you find peace within yourself, you become the kind of person who can live at peace with others."

Mildred Norman Ryder was an American woman who walked across the United States for 28 years to promote peace. She walked with only the clothes on her back, including a blue tunic that read "Peace Pilgrim" on the front and "25,000 Miles on Foot for Peace" on the back. She touched thousands of people by sharing her feelings about peace.

Your Thoughts on Peace
What is peace?

Maya, Age 6

"Peace is quiet and friendship. Everybody gets together and does good things."

Quinn, Age 12

"Peace is loving each other and respecting each other."

Etta, Age 12

"Peace is like harmony. It is everywhere. Working together creates peace."

Natalie, Age 10

"Peace is hope and joy in your heart. It's when everyone gets along."

Logan, Age 12

"Peace to me is respecting other people, the environment, and the world."

Akossiwa, Age 11

"Peace is what you can find within and share with everyone."

How do you find your inner peace?

Rahma, Age 11

"Peace is kindness from everyone's soul. If you want to find peace, don't go looking around for it. It's in you."

Jeremy, Age 6

"I go to my bed and think about things I like to do like play golf."

Joe, Age 7

"Peace is love. You can feel peaceful when you cool down and play a game like Rock, Paper, Scissors, Shoot."

Emily, Age 8

"Peace is when my dog, Hallie, and I are sitting on the lawn together, watching the clouds go by."

Emily, Age 5

"I feel peaceful by doing something relaxing like playing in my room, listening to music, or reading books."

Connor, Age 13

"I go on long walks with my dog or go surfing. They calm me down and let me think about what is making me mad or frustrated."

How can we have peace in the world?

Lydia, Age 12

"If only people could talk things out instead of fighting, their children would grow up knowing peace and be able to teach and spread peace in their lifetimes."

Judith, Age 14

"I think we can have peace in the world if we learn to be peace-makers, be under-standing, be there for one another and lend a hand to those less fortunate."

Hannah, Age 14

"Peace keeps the world going. You have to want it enough."

Ethan, Age 7

"We can create peace by listening to how others feel."

Ruweyda, Age 12

"I think peace is about people, no matter what race, size, or beliefs, putting aside their dif-ferences and working together."

Nicole, Age 11

"I have a dream that there will be no war and everyone will be peaceful and happy. We have to be kind and generous."

Peace Activities

Help your child find their inner peace by working through the following activities *together*.

your picture

Write your own thoughts about peace

Draw your favorite peace symbol or make one of your own

What are some little things you can do to bring peace to others?

Given the activities listed below, talk about those that bring peace and those that create conflict.

Listening to music   Blaming

Teasing   Talking to a special adult

Taking a walk   Drawing a picture

Interrupting   Counting to 10

Quiet Time   Hitting

Riding a bike   Listening

Apologizing   Playing with a pet

Name calling   Bossing a friend

Playing a game   Arguing

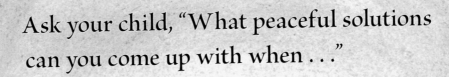
Ask your child, "What peaceful solutions can you come up with when . . ."

1. You accidentally break a friend's favorite toy. They run and tell their parent that you did it on purpose.

2. A girl at school says you have funny ears.

3. Everyone has seen the new movie but you. Your friend tells you that you can't join in the play because you didn't see the movie.

4. You've been angry about something all day and there's no one to talk to.

5. A new kid has just moved to your school who looks very different than what you're used to. You want to be friendly, but you are afraid your friends will leave you.

6. Someone asks you a question that you don't know the answer to and they call you "stupid."

CD Lyrics

In Harmony

by Sue Sheriff
Copyright ©1994

Chorus:
In harmony,
That's how I'd like the world to be,
Living in peace and loving one another.
In harmony, we can all be free
By treating everyone like he's a brother

And although we may have differences
That make us all unique . . .
We all want the same in life—
It's happiness we seek.
Chorus

We all have different faces;
Thoughts and feelings, too.
But we all want a healthy earth
With skies and oceans blue.
Chorus

Some of us need a wheelchair
And some of us cannot hear.
But all we want is to be loved
And live life without fear.
Chorus

Let's celebrate our differences,
Yet find our common ground.
We all deserve life's goodness—
There's enough to go around!
Chorus

What do you think it means to treat everyone
like a brother?

Feel the Peace

by Sue Sheriff
Copyright ©2008

There's a place we can go
That is very deep inside
We are safe, we are whole
And we never have to hide

It's a place in our hearts
Where the noise and chatter cease
It's a place all our own
Where we rest and find our peace

Chorus:
And we listen to the still small voice
The voice that comes from within
And from this very quiet place
We feel the peace and peace is where we begin

Close your eyes, take a breath
Make your breathing very slow
Watch your thoughts floating by
Try your best to let them go

Feel your body very still
There is nothing else to do
Watch your breath in and out
Hear the Truth inside of you
Chorus

When we're feeling so confused
And our thinking is not clear
Listen quietly inside
And the answers will appear

Once we spend a little time
In this very peaceful way
We can go out in the world
Find the joy in every day
Chorus

Meditation is a way to find a peaceful feeling inside.
Can you think of other ways?

Soul Stew

by Sue Sheriff

Well I woke up in the morning
Ideas inside my head
I was so excited
That I jumped right out of bed

And then I ran down to the kitchen
To start my recipe
I grabbed a pot and had the thought
That peace begins with me

Chorus:
I'm making Soul Stew
Do doo do doo doo do
I'm making Soul Stew
Do doo do doo doo do
I'm making Soul Stew
Do doo do doo doo do
I'm making Soul Stew
Do doo do doo doo do

First I add a little kindness
And then forgiveness too
Some friendship and respect
And a lot of love will do

And then I pour a cup of joy
A pinch of harmony
And then a lot of gratitude
For how the world can be
Chorus

This soul food is so good for you
A very special meal
It helps to make peace in our world
It helps our hearts to heal
Chorus

Can you think of other things to add to the recipe?

May All Children

by Ken Guilmartin

May, may all, may all children
May all people everywhere
Hear this prayer
May, may all, may all children
May all people everywhere
Live in peace
Sweet peace

Peaceful minds, peaceful hearts, peace on earth
Sweet peace on earth

This beautiful song offers a prayer for peace.
What would your prayer for the world be?

IN HARMONY

Words and Music by Sue Sheriff

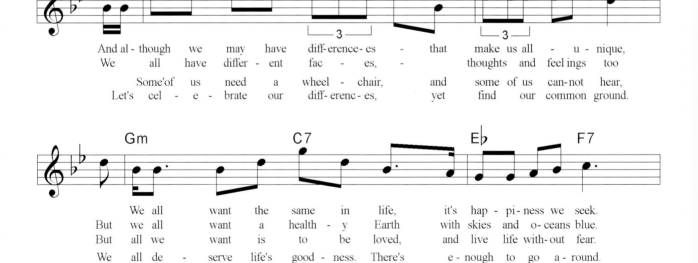